Just Like Grandpa

Text Copyright 2012 by Elizabeth Murphy-Melas
Illustration Copyright 2012 by Mary Kate Wright

Published by Health Press NA Inc.
PO Box 37470
Albuquerque, NM 87176
(505)888-1394
www.healthpress.com

Library of Congress Cataloging-in-Publication Data

Murphy-Melas, Elizabeth.
 Just like grandpa : a story about color vision deficiency / Elizabeth Murphy-Melas; illustrated by Mary Kate Wright.
    p. cm.
 ISBN 978-0-929173-58-0
1. Color vision deficiency in children--Juvenile literature. I. Wright, Mary Kate, 1978- ill. II. Title.

Pediatric color vision test plates reprinted with permission of Dr. Terrace Waggoner.

Foreword

Eight percent of the boys and one half percent of the girls in the world are born color blind. That's as high as one out of twelve boys and one out of two hundred girls.

Many people think anyone labeled as color blind only sees black and white – like watching a black and white movie or television. This is a common misconception and not true. There are many different types (protan, deutan, and tritan) and degrees (mild, moderate, and severe) of color blindness – more correctly called color vision deficiencies. Being color deficient can be a challenge at times. Bill Clinton, past President of the United States, was color deficient and met that challenge. You can, too, by learning about and understanding color vision deficiencies.

Dr. Terrace L. Waggoner
Refractive Surgery Research Coordinator
Naval Aerospace Medical Institute
Pensacola, FL

Introduction

Color vision deficiency (CVD), more commonly known as color blindness, means that one has trouble distinguishing between certain colors. In almost all cases, the confusion is among red, green, blue, or a mixture of these colors. Color blindness is most often caused by a genetic abnormality, although aging, injury to the eye and some medications can affect color vision.

It is important for children, particularly for young boys, that they be tested for CVD as early as five years of age, especially if there is a familial tendency toward the deficiency. Children who have color vision deficiency often experience difficulties in school prior to their diagnosis. Colors are used as teaching tools in reading and math, as well as in activities such as sorting blocks, counting beads, or working with maps and worksheets.

If you suspect your child may be color blind you should make an appointment with a health care professional or pediatric ophthalmologist.

Elizabeth Murphy-Melas

Ben swung his feet back and forth while sitting at his desk. Miss Barker stood in front of the classroom holding a large map. She pinned it to the bulletin board.

"Who can tell me what crayon we should use to color the mountains?" she asked.

Hands flew up.

"Brown," said Susan. She walked up to the map and colored the mountains brown.

"Okay," said Miss Barker. "What about the forests?"

Ben raised his hand. "Green," he said. Ben went to the board and used a red crayon to color the forest.

All the kids giggled and stared at Ben.

"I think a better color would be green," said Miss Barker.

"Ben doesn't know his colors," whispered Tommy loud enough for everyone to hear.

5

Ben felt his face turn warm and walked slowly back to his desk. It was true, he thought. He never got his colors right. His workbook was full of X's from Miss Barker for all his mistakes. On one page, he was supposed to draw a line to all the red balls. Somehow, he got them all wrong.

After school Miss Barker handed Ben a note.

"Please give this to your mom and ask her to call me."

Ben nodded. "I will."

As soon as he got home Ben handed Mom the note. He knew it was about his not knowing his colors like the other kids.

Ben was glad it was Friday and school was over for the week. Tomorrow was Saturday, and Grandpa always came over to see him. Sometimes they went on adventures to the museum, and other times they just read books together or played in the back yard. Ben thought his Grandpa was great! Tomorrow they were supposed to take a nature walk down by the park. Just thinking about it made Ben feel really excited and not so bad about the teacher's note.

The first thing Grandpa said when he saw Ben the next day was, "I like your new red jacket."

"Thanks," said Ben, "but it is brown."

"Actually," Mom said with a funny look on her face, "it's green."

"Hmmm, okay," said Grandpa. "Let's take a walk to the ice cream shop and then we will go to the park."

Ben yelled, "Bye, Mom," and ran out the front door. Mom touched Grandpa on the sleeve.

"I think Ben may be color blind like you," she said. "He is having a lot of trouble at school with learning his colors and the teacher sent me a note suggesting that we have his eyes checked. Keep an eye on him and tell me what you think."

"Okay," said Grandpa. "No problem."

When they got to the ice cream store Grandpa ordered chocolate ice cream and Ben got strawberry. Ben wanted candy sprinkles on his ice cream but he got confused because the lady kept asking him what kind of sprinkles he wanted – brown or pink. They all looked the same to him! Then they walked around the corner to the park and sat on a bench that was under a big group of trees to eat their ice cream cones.

"It's a beautiful fall day and the leaves are really changing colors," said Grandpa.

"Yes," said Ben. "There are so many yellow and brown ones."

"I think there may be some red leaves, too," said Grandpa.

"Are you sure?" Ben asked. "I only see yellow and brown ones." Ben thought Grandpa was joking with him.

They spent a long time walking around the park and Ben got to feed the ducks with some crackers Grandpa had in his pocket before they went home.

Ben was tired when they got home, and Grandpa gave him a big hug. "I will see you next Saturday and we can practice a few soccer moves."

"That will be cool," said Ben and he ran off to his bedroom.

Grandpa stood in the doorway and paused before speaking to Mom. "I think you are right, and that Ben is color blind like me," he said quietly. "Do you remember when you were growing up how much trouble I had with telling different colors apart? I am pretty sure Ben has the same problem seeing red and green," Grandpa added.

"Hmm, okay," said Mom. "He is mixing up colors and he can't match his clothes either. I will call our eye doctor, Dr. Rogers, first thing on Monday."

"Don't worry," Grandpa said with a smile. "Even if he is color blind, I can help him figure out ways to work around it."

That night when Mom was tucking Ben into bed she said, "Ben, I am going to make an appointment for you for an eye exam, just to see if maybe you need glasses. But let's wait and see what the doctor says."

Ben smiled. He hoped this would help him to see colors better.

A few days later Ben's dad took him to see the ophthalmologist, Dr. Rogers. Ben thought that was a big word, but Dad said it just meant he was an eye doctor.

Dr. Rogers had Ben sit in a big chair and examined his eyes using all sorts of lights and charts. He finally said, "Ben, you have excellent vision."

Dad explained how Ben's teacher had sent a note home about his trouble recognizing colors in class. Dad also said that Ben had trouble matching his clothes for school. "Ben has a green book bag, but he always calls it brown," Dad added.

"It is brown," Ben said. "And on the playground the kids tell me to kick the red ball, but it looks brown to me too."

"Ben," said Dr. Rogers, "what you are describing is color vision deficiency. Many people call it being color blind. This means that your vision is good but you can't see some colors. Your eyes see greens, reds, yellows, and oranges differently from some other people's eyes. You might be surprised to know that one out of twelve boys have color vision deficiency. Probably, someone else at your school has it too."

18

√ WHAT DR ROGERS SHOWS BEN ↑   ↑ WHAT BEN SEES ↓

Dr. Rogers took Dad and Ben into another examining room. "I am going to give you a quick and easy eye test for color blindness. Some doctors use the Ishihara Plate test," he said to Ben, "but I have a different one."

Dr. Rogers held up a picture made up of different colored dots. He said that inside the pattern of dots were some shapes. "Can you tell me what shapes you see?" he asked.

Ben stared for a long moment. "I don't see any shapes," he said sighing heavily. Dr. Rogers held up another picture. "Do you see a shape in this one?"

"I just see a lot of dots," Ben replied. Dad pointed to the sailboat inside the pattern of dots, but Ben couldn't see it.

"If you did not have color vision deficiency, you would see a circle, a square, and a star in the first one and the sailboat your Dad showed you in the second one. But don't worry," he said, patting Ben on the back. "All this tells me is that you are red/green color blind which is the most common type. Let me show you this model of your eye."

19

Ben thought the model of an eye was very cool.

"In the back of the retina there are two types of cells called rods and cones. Rod cells help us see at night. They don't see color, which is why we can only see shades of black, grey, and white in the dark. Cone cells are sensitive to brighter light. There are three types and they pick up red, green, and blue colors.

When the colors mix together, we are able to see a rainbow of colors. Your cone cells don't see all the colors."

"Is there any chance his color blindness will go away?" Dad asked.

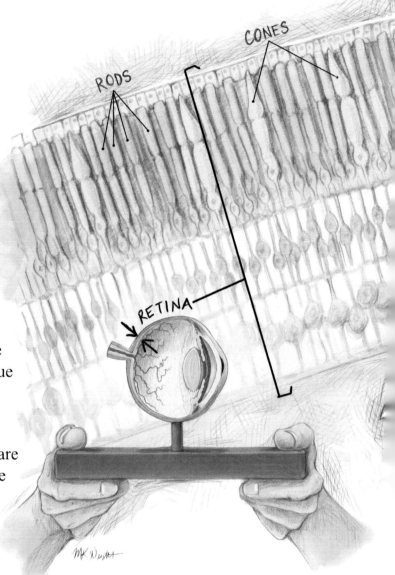

"No," said Dr. Rogers. "But color vision deficiency is not a disease. His eyes are perfectly healthy."

"Why am I color blind?" Ben asked.

"The genes for color blindness would be passed down from your mother. Someone in your mom's family must be color blind too. Just like you inherit genes that determine the color of your eyes and hair, or how tall or short you may be, you also inherit color blindness," said Dr. Rogers.

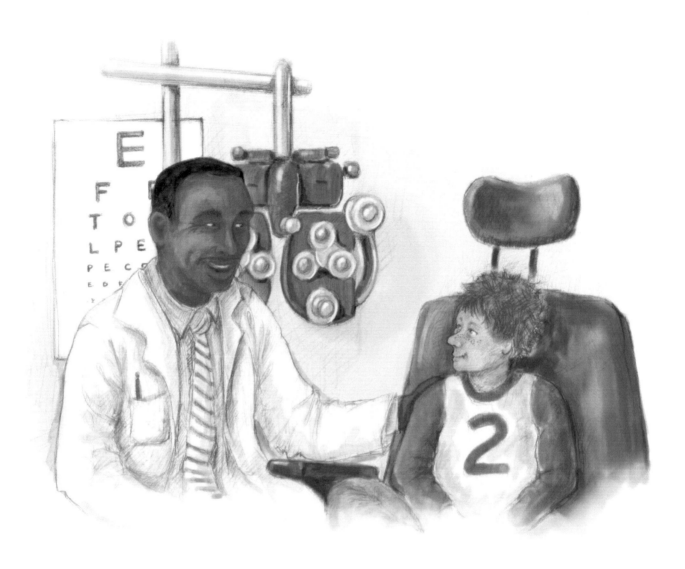

"It would be helpful if you told your teacher at school that you are color blind so she could help you when you have work that involves using colors," he added.

"Gee, at least now I know I'm not dumb," said Ben.

"Oh, no!" said Dr. Rogers. "You are a very smart boy. And the more you and your family understand about color vision deficiency, the easier it will be for you." He smiled at Ben.

"Cool!" said Ben.

Mom was waiting for them when they got home.

"Did you get glasses?" she asked Ben.

"No, Dr. Rogers says my eyes are fine," he replied.

"It turns out he is color blind," said Dad.

"I thought that might be it," said Mom. "Ben, your grandpa is color blind too! I think it would be nice if you and Grandpa got together and talked about it on Saturday."

"Sure," said Ben. "That would be great."

23

That evening after dinner, Ben and Mom sat down on the den floor. They dumped all his crayons, colored pencils, and markers on the carpet.

"What are you guys doing?" asked Dad.

"We are checking to make sure that everything is labeled with the color name so that Ben won't get his crayons and markers mixed up at school," said Mom. Dad was surprised to see that some crayons and markers had the color printed on them, while others did not. They wrote the name of the color on little white labels and then wrapped them around the end of the marker or colored pencil.

The next day Ben and Mom got to school early so they could meet with Miss Barker. Mom explained what they had learned from Ben's visit to the eye doctor. Miss Barker was very understanding and after lunch spoke to the class about color vision deficiency, and also let Ben answer some questions.

"Can you only see black and white?" Tommy asked.

"No," said Ben. "I can see a lot of colors, but mostly get red, green, and brown mixed up because they look almost the same to me."

On Saturday, Grandpa came over to visit. He brought a soccer ball. Ben and Grandpa went to the back yard and kicked the ball around.

"I hear you are having a little problem with your colors," Grandpa said with a smile.

"Yeah," replied Ben. "I hate that stupid color test. At least now I know I'm not dumb because I can't tell red from green and stuff like that."

"Well, Ben, I was about your age when I first learned I was color blind. I used to color things wrong all the time at school! And I had a favorite shirt I liked to wear which I thought was white, but it was really pink! I was teased a lot."

"I think it will be better now at school because my friends know why I get colors mixed up. It still makes me mad that I get confused," said Ben.

"I understand," said Grandpa. "Even today I get my colors mixed up. You will learn little tricks like labeling things with their colors. I remember one time when I was a little boy I stayed outside in the sun too long and got very sunburned. I couldn't tell my skin was turning red. Once your friends and family understand about being color blind they can help you."

"Do you pick out your own clothes to wear? Mom has to help me."

Grandpa chuckled. "I get a little help in that department too. Your grandmother makes sure my clothes and socks match in the morning before I walk out the door. And she never sends me to the grocery store to buy bananas. I have a hard time telling if they are ripe. I have brought home many green bananas!"

That night before he went to bed, Mom got out Ben's clothes for the next day. She sat on the edge of his bed and gave him a hug and kiss.

"Did you enjoy your visit with Grandpa?" she asked.

"It was awesome," said Ben. "You know, I'm just like Grandpa."

"Is that a good thing?" asked Mom.

"Oh yeah," said Ben. "Grandpa and I see things in just the same way!"

Over the next weeks, Ben did much better in school. His classmates helped him pick out the right color crayons, and sometimes Miss Barker gave him different worksheets to do if they involved colors.

Grandpa surprised Ben and came to have lunch at school one day. He and Ben laughed and told funny stories to Ben's friends about mixing up colors.

On a chilly winter's day one Saturday Grandpa, Mom, and Ben took a walk in the park. Snow flurries were gently falling and Ben stuck out his tongue to catch them.

"There sure are some pretty pink snowflakes coming down," Grandpa said to Ben and winked at him.

Ben ran around in circles and giggled.

"Yeah, Grandpa," he said. "I love pink snow!"

Mom just looked at them both and laughed. "Me, too," she said.

Resources

www.aoa.org

This is the official website of the American Optometric Association and provides in-depth medical information about color vision deficiency. This organization also can be contacted at their toll-free number, 800-365-2219.

www.colorvisiontesting.com

This website features online color vision testing plates designed by Dr. Terrace L. Waggoner, one of the leaders in the field of color vision deficiency.

www.everydayhealth.com

An online health information source with general information about color vision deficiency.

www.keepingkidshealthy.com

An online health information source that explains about the x-linked recessive gene that is responsible for color blindness

www.kidshealth.org

KidsHealth claims to be the most-visited site on the Web for information about health, behavior, and development from before birth through the teen years. Run by the Nemours Foundation, this website gives a kid friendly basic explanation about color vision deficiency.

www.preventblindness.org

This is the website for the Prevent Blindness America organization. It offers valuable information about eye care and more general information about color vision deficiency. This organization also can be contacted using their toll free number, 800-331-2020.

www.webmd.com

This online health resource covers many topics including general information about color vision deficiency. This website also discusses alternative lenses and glasses that may help color blind people see more colors.

About the Author

Elizabeth Murphy-Melas, holds a Master's Degree in English Literature from Northern Arizona University. She is the author of a number of special needs books for young children. Her books include *Pennies, Nickels and Dimes*, a story for children concerning liver transplant; *Keeping a Secret: A Story About Juvenile Rheumatoid Arthritis; The Girl With No Hair: A Story About Alopecia Areata,* and *My Blood Brother: A Story About Childhood Leukemia. Just Like Grandpa* is her fifth book published with Health Press NA Inc. Ms. Murphy-Melas wrote the book to help children understand and cope with color vision deficiency. She presently resides in Atlanta, Georgia.

About the Illustrator

Mary Kate Wright is a certified medical illustrator. She holds a Bachelor of Arts from Tulane University and a Master's of Science in Medical Illustration from the Medical College of Georgia. She is sole proprietor of MKIllustrations (www.mkillustrations.com) and has clients from all aspects of the medical and scientific community. Her award-winning work has been published in journals, newspapers, books, brochures, and patient education newsletters, and she has been recognized in the APEX Awards for Publication Excellence, winning the Grand Award in Design and Illustration in 2004 and an Award of Excellence in Illustration and Typography in 2005. Mary Kate is a professional member in the Association of Medical Illustrators, the Guild of Natural Science Illustrators, and the Health and Science Communications Association. She recently became a member of the Society of Children's Book Writers and Illustrators. *Just Like Grandpa* is the third children's book she has illustrated.

Currently Mary Kate and her family live in Hawaii with their two dogs.